THE DAILY BLOG OF HARLEY THE DOG

JODIE K. SARGINSON

Text and Illustrations copyright © 2021 Jodie Sarginson

Published by Toad Publications

Paperback ISBN-13: 978-1-7364227-0-0

eBook ISBN-13: 978-1-7364227-1-7

Hardback ISBN-13: 978-1-7364227-2-4

Library of Congress Control Number: 2021901760

I dedicate this book to my fiancé, Doug Barr, and our kids Dillon (and Morgan) Barr, Nickole Sarginson, and Raelene Barr.
My life would not be the same without all of you in it. Thank you for always believing in me and my crazy ideas. Each one of you has been a driving force behind this book in your own way and for that I say I love you and thank you! I cannot forget our sweet Harley girl. I never knew having a dog would be so much fun. You fill our lives with so much joy!
Thank you to all of my family and friends who encouraged me to keep on writing posts about Harley. Thank you for letting me share our funny, lovable, and mischievous pup with you!

My name is Jodie Sarginson and I live in the beautiful city of Port Huron, Michigan. I was born and raised in Flint, Michigan. I moved to Port Huron in 2017 to live with my fiancé, Doug Barr, after my daughter Nickole Sarginson, moved away to college. I'd been with Doug since 2009, so it only made sense to move. Doug has two children, Dillon and Raelene Barr. Raelene lives with us and Dillon lives with his fiancé, Morgan, in Colorado.

When Raelene went to visit Dillon and Morgan, they called me and asked me on a scale of 1-10 when I was getting a dog. I said, "ZERO!" Raelene was heading off to college, Nickole was going to be a senior in college, and Dillon and Morgan were already set to begin a life together—Doug and I were going to be empty-nesters!

Fast forward a few days later, Doug asked me about rescuing a Pit Bull puppy. His cousin's daughter rescued a Pit Bull momma and her ten puppies. They were looking for homes for the puppies. Although I was not thrilled by the fact, I couldn't say no. The puppies needed fur-ever homes, so you guessed it—WE GOT A DOG!

Our dog's name is Harley (she's a girl). She has truly been a blessing to our family. She has the funniest personality which I capture through photos. I started sharing the photos on social media with little blurbs, as if I knew what Harley was thinking. As time went on, multiple people suggested I write a book and I decided to give it some thought. The encouragement I received from Doug, Dillon, Nickole, and Raelene was amazing, so I jumped in with two feet and here I am with my first published book.

I'm excited for this journey and I wanted to thank you as the reader for coming along on this ride with me.

Take care,

Jodie

1 / HI, MY NAME IS HARLEY GRACE BARR AND I AM A DOG

Hı, my name is Harley Grace Barr and I AM A DOG! It's fun being a dog, so I want to share my thoughts with you! There are just a few things I need to tell you before you start reading my blog.

1. I'm a dog, so I have no idea how to count (you will see what I mean when I try to keep up on what day it is).

2. I really do love all of the humans in my life, but I especially like to pick on my human, Jodie.

3. I'm sharing my blog with you because the world needs a little bit more laughter... especially these days.

4. Have *you* ever pretended to think like your animal? If not, you should try it for a good laugh!

5. I hope it brings a smile to your face (like it does mine)!

2 / PUPPY IN A DISH

DAY 1

    I heard I was going to a fur-ever home. I didn't know exactly what it meant; all I knew was I felt at peace, so I dreamt of what it would be like...

    I think it will be like a big bowl of endless dog food and I will always have a full belly. I really don't think it gets any better than that!

3 / MEETING MY HUMANS

Day 20 🐕

This is the day I met my HUMANS. 💕

I instantly knew the lady in the green shirt was going to be a talker (YIKES). I wondered if the other two humans *rescued* me so I could *rescue* them from her constant babbling. All I know is that this is going to be interesting!

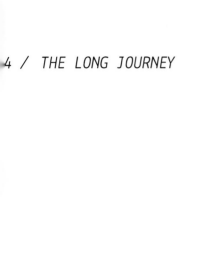

4 / THE LONG JOURNEY

Day 20 1/2

This was my long journey to my fur-ever home. I must be dreaming of that full bowl of food because my tongue is sticking out.

What do you dream about?

made it to my fur-ever home! This is my human Raelene. She seems nice.

DAY 45

Human Jodie and human Doug took me to the pet store today to get me toys, treats, a collar, a bed, and a new leash. I was so excited because they really *hyped* it up for me. Well, I got a little overwhelmed and my sweet human Doug just sat with me in the middle of the floor.

Do you ever feel overwhelmed?

DAY 65

I had to go to school. Human Jodie said something about "making me more disciplined." Maybe she should go back to school. I'm sure the only teacher comment on her report cards was "TALKS TOO MUCH!" Well, I played the part and I graduated!

This is *boring*. All of the other dogs get to do fun things; I have to learn how to sit. 😠

Follow up on the sitting—I NAILED IT!

DAY 87

Soooo, this is me and my human Doug. He said we were going for a walk around the backyard. I just want to point out that *I do not have a leash on.*

This is important and you will see why in the following pages. These were the good ol' days. NO leash, some trust, and I could run as fast as I wanted to! What do you like to do outside?

DAY 90

I took a long road trip with my humans to visit my human Nickole at college (they sure like to travel).

College life can be exhausting. I mean, I enjoyed my time, but honestly, don't know how those college kids do it!

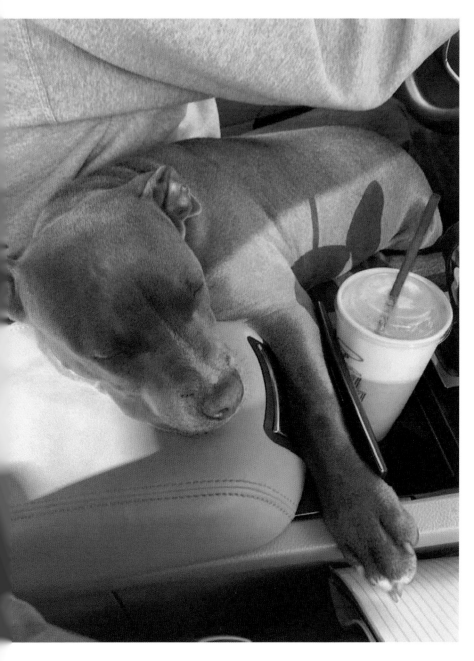

I wanted to stay awake because I didn't want to miss anything (minus
uman Jodie babbling... I don't miss that AT ALL when I'm sleeping 😌). I
ist couldn't keep my eyes open 🐾. Do you get sleepy during car rides?

DAY 96

I went to a hockey game last night. It was fun! I thought it was odd that a bunch of humans were in this fenced yard chasing each other and chasing this small round thing. I think I heard human Doug call it a "puck." Anyways, I wonder if this is what humans think my pup pals and I look like when we are at the dog park! Have you ever been to a hockey game?

Hey human Doug, I think I see a pretzel. Do you think that other human ill mind if I have a bite? 🐾

DAY 33

Human Doug is so nice to me. He taught me how to drive! Human Jodie didn't think it was a good idea because she said I'm a dog and dogs don't drive. 🙄

I don't want to say it but... human Jodie was right. I'm not cut out for this driving stuff—I'm TIRED! 😴

11 / JUST SITTING IN MY BIG GIRL
    DIAPER

DAY 101

Just sitting here deep in thought. I wonder if my humans want to play that fun game where I find something I know I can't have and I put it in my mouth and run around and everyone chases me. I love when they all cheer for me when they yell, "HARLEY!"

Just sitting in my diaper because I'm becoming a "big girl" dog now.

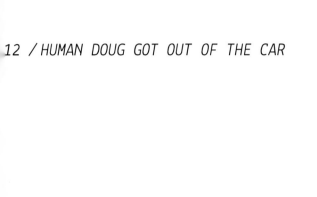

12 / HUMAN DOUG GOT OUT OF THE CAR

DAY 323

Last night I was super upset because my human Doug GOT OUT OF THE CAR and didn't take me (and left me with chatty Kathy 🙍). I refused to look at human Jodie (she kept calling my name, but I was like, "NOPE! NOT GONNA HAPPEN.") Anyways, my feelings are hurt (and so are my ears now—honestly, this lady is never quiet!)

I refuse to look. Why me? 😢

13 / GOING ROGUE

DAY 263 🐾

I'm currently pouting because my humans don't trust me anymore and I have to be on a leash at ALL TIMES. I decided to go off on a little adventure. I chased squirrels 🐿 and rabbits 🐇 and ran in and out of peoples' yards and down the street and I had *so much fun*! When my humans caught up to me, they were NOT HAPPY. Human Jodie did her normal babble and a little bit of what I think is called a lecture. 🐾

Insert heavy sigh…

Anyways, human Doug was so scared and just kept hugging me (human Jodie did hug me right after her lecture 😊). BUT, long story short, they have me on a short leash. 🐕 It's not nearly as much fun as my adventure. ☹ I told you that one time I ran without a leash was important to me!

Geez... I just wanted to have some fun!

Is the leash REALLY necessary?

. . .

14 / GOVERNOR ISSUED A STAY-AT-HOME
   ORDER

DAY 130

My human Jodie just told me that the governor issued a Stay-At-Home order and said I cannot go to the dog park, which makes me sad. 😢 I'm not sure how much more I can take of these humans constantly in my business. They even watch when I do "my business" outside. 🙈 It's so embarrassing. They announce to each other, "She went number one and two!"

I'm like, "WHAT? I don't announce when they do these things." 🙍‍♀️ Have you ever been sad or embarrassed?

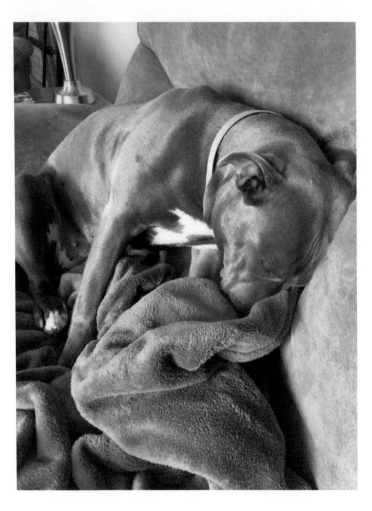

15 / WITH JODIE DURING QUARANTINE

DAY 436 🐕

Human Jodie thinks we are BFFs now that I have been forced to listen to her talk for countless hours due to being stuck in the house since March (I think that's the month she said). She said,"Harley, smile for the picture" and this is the best smile I could muster up to show my enthusiasm. I wonder if there's a new home for my human Jodie. I think in the dog world, they call it being re-homed. Anyways, *I'm* not going anywhere because I love my home, but I'm not opposed to letting my human Jodie try out a few other places to live. 😐

Ummm... where did my ears go? 😬

Oh, the excitement I feel. 🙄

16 / MISSING MY PUPPY PALS

DAY 583

I'm just sitting here thinking 🌚, *If I find a way to open the door, I will take myself to the dog park to meet up with my friends.* My humans have been busy. I know my pup pals probably miss me, and I sure do miss them. Do you ever miss your friends?

DAY ???

I can't remember because all of the days are running together now.

My human Jodie is at it again and talking to me. She was talking, and despite my heavy sigh, she just kept talking. I even looked away (actually, I was thinking about chasing squirrels and jumping up to get the birds as they fly away, going on an adventure without the leash—so many things I wish I was doing instead of being her emotional support quarantine dog). What are some of your favorite things to do?

18 / I JUST CAN'T

THIS WILL BE A QUICK UPDATE. Picture 1 is human Jodie talking to me. When she says, "Harley listen, I need to talk about a few things," this is my look of "WHY MUST IT BE ME YOU TALK TO!"

What I would like to do is sit quietly on the couch without being bothered and watch my TV shows, but no! I am stuck listening to the "few" things human Jodie needs to talk about.

Picture 2 is me having ENOUGH of human Jodie talking to me. 👧

Someone come and pick her up please! 🤞

I'm listening.

I can't. I'm done!

19 / THAT TIME I TRIED TO NAP
DURING COVID

DAY 787

Soooooo, my human Jodie was talking to me as I was trying to nap (I love my naps). She would not stop talking, so I decided to listen to her babble. I don't really understand a lot of human talk, but whatever she said must have been funny, because she laughed at herself.

Do you like to take naps?

Apparently, the only way to quiet human Jodie is to give her some attention.

DAY 212

I just wanted to say *good morning* ☀, and I wanted you to know that I LUB TO GET MY BELLY RUBBED. My human Jodie might get on my nerves at times, *but* at times like these—she is my bestest friend. 💕

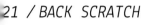

21 / BACK SCRATCH

DAY 23

This is me enjoying some quiet time, some "me" time! Do you ever need quiet time or alone time?

22 / HOW TO RESPOND TO AN OVER-
    TALKER

DAY 447

This is my step-by-step reaction to human Jodie talking to me again, so you can see what I have to put up with.

1. Look at her like, "Here we go again."

2. Throw my head back like, " Please no, not again!"

3. Move my head ever so slightly and pretend my eyes are closed an think, *Maybe this will trick her like I'm sleeping.*

4. And finally, just PLAY DEAD! For sure she will get the point!

23 / JUST A TIRED DOG

DAY 147

I'm just a tired dog and I just want to go to bed! 😴

Today I went to the park with human Raelene, went for a walk with human Doug, chased the cats around the house (I really want to be friends with them now BUT NO, they don't want to be friends 😒). As I tried to lay down and close my eyes—you guessed it, 👱 human Jodie wanted to talk about how her day went. 🙍

What time do you go to bed?

DAY 849

Well, I think the only way to prove that I am done listening to human Jodie's constant babble is to just turn away and stare at the cupboards. 🙍‍♀️

I honestly don't know what else to do. 🙍‍♀️

25 / THAT TIME I ALMOST THOUGHT
   HUMAN JODIE WAS INTERESTING

DAY 743

I must admit—today's story from human Jodie started out interesting. You can see it in my face; I was definitely INTERESTED.

THEN, as she continued to babble I thought, *WAIT... is she being serious?*

Then I realized she was just doing her normal babble.

I'm just so bummed because I thought we were turning a corner with h
stories. 😬

DAY 286

Today I had a pep talk (or is it called a pup talk? 🤔).

Anyways, I looked in the mirror and I said, "You got this girl. You are a dog blogger. The humans want to hear you speak. Be the best you can ever be —and dang girl, you are looking good." 💁

Until next time, people.

Printed in Great Britain
by Amazon

13632481R00051